"Why Wasn't I Told?"

This is a book about personal success and how to achieve it.

Have you ever dreamed about being a celebrity, a singer, a sports star or a famous author?

Have you *seriously* considered the fact that you can be anything you really want to be?

Most of us don't, but we should. The type of success you want is available to you if you are prepared to learn how to attain it.

This book will help you to decide what you want in life and how to go about achieving it.

It could even transform your life into an exciting journey of success.

*This book is dedicated to my parents
who loved me unconditionally and taught me
that I could do anything in life I wanted to do
if I was prepared to work for it.*

"Why Wasn't I Told?"

A Goal Setting Program For Young Adults And Anyone Who Hasn't Been Told Yet

By Lisa Jane McInnes

CASSETTE LEARNING
SYSTEMS
7 Panorama Court
Bulleen 3105
Victoria, Australia.
Phone (03) 850 1492
Fax   (03) 852 0498

WHY WASN'T I TOLD?
First published in Australasia in 1986 by
Cassette Learning Systems Pty Ltd
7 Panorama Court, Bulleen, Victoria 3105, Australia

Reprinted 1987 (twice)
Reprinted 1988
Reprinted 1989 (twice)
Reprinted 1990
Reprinted 1991 (twice)
Reprinted 1993

Produced by Cassette Learning Systems
Illustrations by Robyn Wearing Smith

The author would like to give special thanks to
Brian & Linda Rudd for their valued assistance and
Robyn Wearing Smith for the wonderful illustrations.

National Library of Australia
Cataloguing in Publication data

McInnes, Lisa Jane, 1959,
    "Why Wasn't I Told?"

   2nd ed.
   Includes index.
   ISBN 0 9588604 1 6.

   1. Self-actualisation (psychology).
   2. Life skills.
   3. Success. I. Title.

158'.1

Typeset in Australia by L.R. Graphics
Printed in Australia by Globe Press

TABLE
OF
CONTENTS

It is always the adventurers who accomplish great things.

TABLE
OF
CONTENTS (Cont'd)

WHAT IS GOAL SETTING?

Goal Setting is the process of systematically writing down your goals and deciding how to achieve them.

What is a goal? It's something you want to do, or have, or become, that is more important than the effort and time necessary for its achievement. Or in other words, it's something you want badly enough that you're prepared to give your time and your effort to accomplish it.

Why have goals? To give yourself some positive measure of your progress in life. Life without goals is like basketball without goal rings. You have no way of measuring your success.

What is success? I see it as the continual achievement of worthy goals.

Why write your goals down? Because it makes you state clearly what you want in life and commit yourself to achieving them.

The pain of discipline is so much better than the pain of regret.

14 GUIDELINES FOR GOAL SETTING

These guidelines have been devised and utilised by thousands of successful people all over the world. They have stood the test of time and are more relevant today than ever.

1. ## IDENTIFY THE PURPOSE FOR YOUR LIFE.
   This is the one thing that all successful people have in common, a strong sense of purpose for their lives.

2. ## DECIDE WHAT YOU WANT TO ACHIEVE IN YOUR LIFE AND WRITE IT DOWN AS IF IT IS ALREADY HAPPENING.
   Writing it ensures that you *clearly* describe what you want and you commit yourself to its achievement. It needs to be written in the positive, present tense so that your mind accepts it.

3. ## LIST THE BENEFITS OF ACHIEVING EACH GOAL
   If you write down 20 good reasons for accomplishing each goal you'll find you'll have all the motivation you need to achieve them. Motivation comes from desire, and desire is a result of knowing the benefits you'll enjoy.

4. ## PLACE AN ACHIEVEMENT TIME ON YOUR GOALS.
   This stops procrastination and assists you to do something constructive each day towards achieving your goals.

5. ## WRITE OUT A DETAILED LIST OF ALL THE THINGS YOU NEED TO DO TO ACHIEVE EACH GOAL.
   Doing this can convert a seemingly impossible goal into bite size chunks you can conquer. Remember "inch by inch, anything's a cinch."

6. ## WRITE DOWN THE OBSTACLES YOU KNOW YOU'LL HAVE TO OVERCOME.
   As you work towards your goal, there will be extra obstacles you weren't aware of at the start. Just accept that problems must be solved every day in life, and take up the challenge to solve them enthusiastically. Successful people are valuable to everyone because they're simply good problem solvers. Problems are another opportunity to stretch your abilities and bring exciting challenges into your life. Become an excellent problem solver.

7. REMOVE THE NEGATIVE INFLUENCES FROM YOUR LIFE.

Be aware of the information going into your mind at all times. So much negative input slips in when we're not monitoring it. Negative information can be found in song lyrics, newspapers, radio broadcasting, television programs, movies and other people's conversation. When you know this information isn't helping you to become a better person, turn it off or move away from it.

8. IMAGINE YOURSELF ACHIEVING YOUR GOAL.

Paint a picture in your head of exactly what it will be like to achieve each goal. See your picture in full colour and complete detail. Imagine how you would feel and think. See if you can make the picture come so alive that you can nearly smell it, hear it, taste it, touch it as well as see it.

9. LIST THE PEOPLE WHOSE HELP YOU'LL NEED.

No–one is able to succeed alone, especially if your definition of success involves building friendships or good working relationships.
We either work with people (as with most jobs) or work for them, especially if your business provides a product or service for others. List carefully, the people whose help you'll need immediately, and those whose help or knowledge you'd like in the future. Don't try to re–invent the wheel. Use other peoples' expertise.

10. DEFINE THE KNOWLEDGE YOU'LL NEED TO SUCCEED.

Try to list the books you'll need to read, the courses you'll need to take and any material you'll need to view or listen to. Put them in an order of priority and get started.

11. ACT NOW!

Nothing works until you do. All the dreaming, scheming and planning mean nothing until you start doing. It's the opening of page one and reading it that starts you learning. Being successful means acting while the crowd's still talking. Your ship won't come in until you send one out.

12. DISCIPLINE YOURSELF.

This means doing what is required for progress, everyday. Replace bad habits with good habits. To lose weight you must exercise and eat correctly. You must rid yourself of poor eating habits and replace them with good ones. If your desire to succeed is strong you will enjoy the benefits of self–discipline. Remind yourself "if it is to be, it is up to me."

13. READ YOUR GOALS OFTEN.

Read them at least 3 times everyday, first thing in the morning, last thing at night, and any relaxed moment during the day when you can take a minute to visualise the achievement of your goals. Try and feel how good those successes will be each time you read your goals.

14. KEEP ADDING NEW GOALS.

It's better to have too many goals than not enough. Life is exciting if there is always another challenge to undertake, another bridge to cross or another mountain to climb. Remove any goals that no longer interest you and make sure you have some goals in every area of your life. When you reach the top of one ladder, you need another one to climb.

Either I will find a way or I will make one.

THE REASONS WHY MOST PEOPLE FAIL TO ACHIEVE WHAT THEY WANT IN LIFE

1. They lack a strong purpose for their life.

2. They don't aim to be better than average.

3. They can't be bothered to educate themselves in the areas in which they are most interested.

4. They don't control their negative thoughts nor their bad habits. This is a lack of self-discipline.

5. They put up with (tolerate) poor health caused by self abuse such as overeating, poor work habits, lack of exercise, smoking and misuse of alcohol and drugs.

6. They procrastinate i.e. they are all talk and no action.

7. They lack persistence. When the going gets tough, most people give up.

8. They have a negative attitude which stops them from seeing the potential or positive possibilities in any situation.

9. They don't control their sexual energy and convert it into creative efforts.

10. They are always looking for "something for nothing" instead of concentrating on working for what they want.

11. They don't make prompt decisions and stick to them.

12. They don't learn to overcome the six most common fears.
    — fear of poverty
    — fear of criticism
    — fear of poor health
    — fear of losing the love of someone they love
    — fear of old age
    — fear of death

THE REASONS WHY MOST PEOPLE FAIL TO ACHIEVE WHAT THEY WANT IN LIFE (Cont'd)

13. They select a poorly suited mate which leads to misery and unhappiness. They don't select someone who shares their same interests, standards and dreams.

14. They are never willing to take a chance.

15. They work with people who neither inspire them nor motivate them to achieve all that they can.

16. They accept superstition and prejudice, which closes their mind and creates fear.

17. They stay in a career they don't like.

18. They don't concentrate all their efforts on one definite aim.

LOVE NEVER FAILS
1 Cor. 13:8 (G.N.B.)

THE REASONS WHY MOST PEOPLE FAIL TO ACHIEVE WHAT THEY WANT IN LIFE (Cont'd)

19. They don't learn how to handle money which means they're always in fear of poverty.

20. They lack enthusiasm. They don't show others that they're particularly interested in anything.

21. They never listen to anyone else's views on religion, politics or racial discrimination. This is commonly known as intolerance.

22. They don't co–operate with others.

23. They are given power that was not earned through their personal efforts, and then they are always in fear of losing it. (So don't spend your time envying what others have been given.)

24. They are intentionally dishonest, which eventually leads to a bad reputation and perhaps the loss of their freedom.

25. They are egotistic and vain. The people with these traits are totally obsessed with themselves and care nothing about others.

26. They guess instead of thinking or getting the facts. If you don't know what you're talking about, stop and listen to others.

27. They forget to ask for God's help.

28. They forget to show other people that they love them, by spending time with them.

The mind is
not a rubbish
tin, so don't
feed it garbage.

Life is like a smorgasbord. Your plate, it runneth over!
But don't take the left overs if it leaves no room for all
the good things.

MY PURPOSE IN LIFE

It has been proven throughout the history of mankind that the major key to successful living is knowing your purpose in life.

If you don't decide what your purpose is, you could spend all your days without direction, without achievement, without self satisfaction and hence without happiness.

Consider the points below when writing down your purpose. These are a collection of ideas taken from successful happy people. Keep in mind that you are a unique individual with a combination of God-given talents like no-one else.

KEY POINTS TO CONSIDER:

to learn to like and love myself
to learn to love and respect others
to learn to know and love God
to learn to be peaceful inside
to develop a positive attitude
to be thankful for the beautiful world God has created

to make the world a better place
to help others
to achieve something everyday
to give 100% effort in everything I do
to learn something new everyday

I asked of life,
"What have you to offer me?"
And the answer came,
"What have you to give?"

PURPOSE

What is your main purpose in life? Write it down and put the date next to it. You can also write down several purposes and number them in order of importance. Your major purpose will be an underlying premise for all your goals.

DATE   PURPOSE

_____

_____

_____

_____

You are a child of the universe, no less than the
trees and the stars.
You have a right to be here.
And whether or not it is clear to you.
No doubt the universe is unfolding as it should.

Desiderata

DO YOU KNOW WHAT YOU WANT IN LIFE?

Take time to dream. It is only when you take time away from people and the rush of life around you, that you really have time to evaluate what's most important to you.

In quiet moments we can let our minds drift to activities we like or projects we want to do. A happy life means working at tasks we think are important and worthwhile. Ask yourself, *"What type of lifestyle do I want?"*

Do you like to work alone or with a team of people?
Do you want to build many friendships or only a few?
Do you want to work for someone else or work for yourself at some stage?
Do you want to work from 9 a.m. to 5 p.m. or a variety of hours?
Do you want to be an expert at anything?
Do you want to spend some time each day learning about your favourite subject?
Do you want some quiet time alone each day?
Do you want to travel often? Where to?
Do you want to belong to a family of people?

We should make time at the end of each week and month to re–evaluate the way we're thinking and the things we're doing. This is to check that we're really doing the things in life that count the most.

Whether you think you can or you can't, you're right!

18

MY FUTURE

Take your time and describe your vision for yourself on these pages. Write it as if it's already happening to you. Use words like "I am", "it is" or "I am enjoying." This is called writing it in the present tense.

NOTE An intelligent person aims at wise action, but a fool starts off in many directions.

Prov. 17:24 (G.N.B.)

_____

_____

_____

_____

_____

_____

_____

_____

_____

_____

_____

God said, "Your task is to build a better world."
I answered, "But the world is so large and complicated
now, and I am so small. There's nothing I can do."
But God in all His wisdom said "Just build a better you!"

MY UNIQUE DIFFERENCES

You are a unique and special individual. You're a masterpiece of God whether you know it or not. There are characteristics about you that identify your uniqueness, like your fingerprints. No-one else in the world has your fingerprints. I want you to list those things which you are most self-conscious about and start thinking of ways to use them to your advantage.

My 6' 2" girlfriend with size 11 shoes always cracks jokes about her 'petite body' which causes a lot of laughter and fun for everyone, but especially eases the pain of her own self-consciousness.

Many pop stars and movie stars have also capitalised on their differences to promote their careers. Paul Hogan took advantage of his working background on the Sydney Harbour Bridge and turned it into part of his T.V. humour.

List what's different about you and how you can turn it into an advantage.

_____

_____

_____

_____

_____

_____

_____

_____

Learning to love yourself is the greatest love of all.

sung by Whitney Houston

MY UNIQUE DIFFERENCES

"Peace comes from enjoying what you have and by losing the desire for what you cannot have."

TAKING STOCK OF MYSELF

Many people are not satisfied with what they've been given in life. However, we should be thankful for what we've got. We're not meant to be perfect. But we are meant to make the very best of what we have.

List all your good points in the space below. This is called taking stock of how you see yourself right now. This will also help you to decide how you want to be in the future.

_____

_____

_____

_____

_____

Never forget the value of one human being.

MY ASSETS, ABILITIES & TALENTS

List what you feel are your assets, talents and abilities. You should include any skills you have or sports you can play or activities you're good at.

_____

_____

_____

_____

_____

Great people are just ordinary people with great determination.

TAKING STOCK — MY CHARACTER

CHECKLIST   (Tick the ones which describe you.
                      Put an 'I' next to the ones you want to improve.)

I am honest ✓
I am truthful ✓
I am kind ✓
I am caring ✓
I am trustworthy ✓
I am confident ✓
I am loving
I am respectful ✓
I am flexible
I am reliable ✓
I am enthusiastic ✓
I am cheerful ✓
I am tolerant ✓
I am persuasive
I am affectionate ✓
I am creative ✓
I am curious ✓
I am ambitious
I am generous
I am considerate
I am patient
I am unique
I am happy
I am friendly
I am healthy
I am active
I am smart
I am interesting
I am faithful

Add any others you feel are appropriate

I am persistent
I am happy
I am friendly
I am decisive
I am positive
I am smart
I am interesting
I am faithful
I am obedient
I am open-minded

There is nothing so powerful as the truth.

TAKING STOCK — MY ASSETS & ABILITIES

CHECKLIST (Tick the ones which describe you. Put an 'I' next to the ones you want to improve. Add any others you can think of.)

ASSETS
good eyesight
good sense of smell
good sense of taste
good hearing
good balance
good co-ordination
good sense of rhythm
good sense of touch
strong limbs
flexible joints
firm muscles
reasonable body shape
pleasant face
two legs
two arms
healthy hair
good teeth

ABILITIES & TALENTS
I can draw
I can paint
I can knit
I can sew
I can act
I can sing in tune
I can whistle
I can skate
I can dance
I can ski
I can swim
I can horseride
I can trampoline
I can run
I can ride a bike
I can play an instrument
I can read music
I can write songs
I can write poetry
I can cook a meal
I can fix a chair
I can grow vegetables
I can fix toys
I can take good photographs
I can make pottery
I can do yoga
I can do aerobics
I can jump high
I can throw far
I can play racquet sports
I can play ball sports

Most of life is getting ready.

TAKING STOCK

Ask your parents and friends to describe you as they see you. Get them to write a list of your good points and your bad points. This will ensure that your view of yourself is in perspective.

Accept me as I am so I may learn what I can become.

REVIEW

A GOAL IS _____

_____

_____

_____

GOALS ARE IMPORTANT BECAUSE _____

_____

_____

_____

MY DEFINITION OF SUCCESS IS _____

_____

_____

_____

_____

_____

_____

Ask and you will receive;
seek and you will find;
knock and the door will
be opened to you.
Matthew 7:7 (G.N.B.)

GOAL SETTING CATEGORIES

Goal setting is much easier when you divide your life into different categories.

Tick the categories you want to work on.

1. *Personal Improvements I'd Like To Make.*
2. *My Health, Fitness and Well-Being.*
3. *My Family Relationships.*
4. *Building The Spiritual Side Of Me.*
5. *My Friendships.*
6. *My Feelings.*
7. *Careers I'd Like To Try.*
8. *Leisure Activities I'd Like To Do.*
9. *Things I Want To Learn About.*
10. *People I'd Like To Meet.*
11. *People I'd Like To Learn From.*
12. *Ways I'd Like To Serve my Community.*
13. *Ways I'd Like To Serve My Country.*
14. *Books I'd Like To Read.*
15. *Places I'd Like To Go.*
16. *Things I'd Like To Own.*
17. *The Traits I'd Like In A Partner.*
18. *Plans I'd Like To Carry Out.*
19. *Special Problems I'd Like To Solve.*
20. *Ideas I'd Like To Develop.*

How great it is to have the freedom to dream and the power to make those dreams come true.

GOALS I'M ALREADY WORKING TOWARDS

List any goals that you're currently working towards but haven't yet written down.

Direct   Distributor

Better   Tennis   player/pro !

20 bls. lighter + stronger

Challenging Career (

Healthy family

Succcess is a journey.

PERSONAL IMPROVEMENTS I'D LIKE TO MAKE

Tick the goals which are relevant to you, then add your own.

CONFIDENCE — *I am increasing my self-confidence every day.*

ATTITUDE — *I wake up happy each morning*
I am cheerful with everyone

APPEARANCE — *I dress with care*
I'm always looking my best

HYGIENE — *My personal hygiene is important to me*
I floss the teeth I want to keep

SPEECH — *I pronounce each word correctly and use proper English*
I only use language that represents my standards

POSTURE — *I stand erect and sit straight*
I walk tall and confidently

MANNERS — *I am improving my manners every day*
When I'm unsure of correct etiquette, I ask

KINDNESS — *I build people up, rather than criticise them*
I give praise and credit whenever I can

HONESTY — *I am honest, but tactful, with my family and friends*

SELF–CONTROL — *I react to all situations calmly and thoughtfully.*
I choose to be patient, peaceful and forgiving

OTHERS

_____

_____

_____

_____

I may not be the best looking in the group, but I'm always looking my best.

PERSONAL IMPROVEMENTS I'D LIKE TO MAKE

NOTE   A gentle answer quiets anger, but a harsh one stirs it up.   *Prov. 15:1 (G.N.B.)*

      Sensible people always think before they act, but stupid people advertise
      their ignorance.   *Prov. 13:16 (G.N.B.)*

Describe the personal improvements you'd like to make in your life.

_____

_____

_____

_____

_____

_____

_____

_____

_____

_____

_____

_____

Clothes may not make
the man
but they certainly
introduce him.

MY HEALTH, FITNESS AND WELL-BEING

Good health should be a top priority, something you work on everyday. It's difficult to be an achiever when you lack energy due to eating poor quality food and doing no exercise. It's easier to be a dynamic success when you feel good.

Tick the goals you'd like for yourself and add your own goals.

I am improving my health, fitness and well-being everyday.

I walk (run, jog, ride, skip) for twenty minutes each day.

I read a page a day about how to eat better, live better or feel better.

I eat and enjoy food that is good for me.

All glory comes from daring to begin.

MY HEALTH, FITNESS AND WELL-BEING

NOTE   Being cheerful keeps you healthy. It is slow death to be gloomy all the time.

Prov. 17:22 (G.N.B.)

Write your own health goals here.

_____

_____

_____

_____

_____

There's no such
thing as "can't!"

MY FAMILY RELATIONSHIPS

Families are the most important unit in society. They are a place to grow, to learn and to love.

God made us to be son or daughter, husband or wife, and father or mother. Respect and treasure your family regardless of the difficulties and problems you may face with them. The greatest book of all time, the Bible, tells us to honour our father and mother.

WAYS I'D LIKE TO IMPROVE MY FAMILY RELATIONSHIPS.

Underline the goals which are relevant to you, then add your own.

COMMUNICATION
I am improving the way I speak to my parents, my brothers and my sisters.
I always say something nice, or I say nothing at all.

TREATMENT
I treat others the way I want them to treat me.
I try to see all discussions from my parents point of view so that I can better understand their decisions.
I listen to the opinions of my brothers and sisters and give them consideration.

SHARING
I am willing to share whatever I have with my family because they are more important than things.

BEHAVIOUR
I am helpful around the house and I don't expect my parents to do everything for me.

_____

_____

_____

Happiness is found along the way, not at the end of the road.

MY FAMILY RELATIONSHIPS

NOTE   Discipline your children while they are young enough to learn. If you don't,
you are helping them destroy themselves.   *Prov. 19:18 (G.N.B.)*

Write your family goals here.

_____

_____

_____

_____

The love in your heart wasn't put there to stay.
Love isn't love till you give it away.

BUILDING THE SPIRITUAL SIDE OF ME

God created each of us as unique and special individuals. He gave us a magnificient world to live in, and put love in our hearts. Successful people know the importance of spending quiet time alone with God. They take time to thank Him, to ask for His help and to read His word.

Earl Nightingale, an acclaimed author, said that we could become highly successful by reading just two books. They are the dictionary and the Bible. Why not give it a try.

Underline the goals relevant to you and add your own.

I take time to appreciate the beautiful world God has made.

I learn about God each day by reading the Bible.

I make time to pray each day.

I take time to be still and listen to God.

To have found God is not the end of your search, but the beginning.

BUILDING THE SPIRITUAL SIDE OF ME

NOTE   Peace is what I leave with you; it is my own peace that I give you. I do not
give it as the world does. Do not be worried and upset; do not be afraid.

John 14:27 (G.N.B.)

Write your spiritual goals here.

_____

_____

_____

_____

_____

_____

_____

_____

_____

_____

_____

_____

Help me to remember Lord that nothing's going to
happen today that you and me can't handle together.

MY FRIENDSHIPS

Friends are people who care about you, enjoy your company and are willing to stay with you in good times and bad.

Friendships form because people either respect you, share common interests with you, or simply enjoy themselves when you're around.

We should try to earn peoples friendship rather than just expect it. We earn it by being a caring and sharing person without expecting anything back.

NOTE   Friends always show their love.
        Prov. 17:17 (G.N.B.)

WAYS I'D LIKE TO IMPROVE MY FRIENDSHIPS

Tick any goals relevant to you and add your own.

I am an honest and trustworthy friend.

I avoid gossip and speak positively of my friends always.

I give my time to help my friends.

I am reliable and considerate.

Be true to your word, your work and your friend.

MY FRIENDSHIPS

Describe the type of friendships you would like to build and the traits you'd like in a friend.

_____

_____

_____

_____

_____

_____

Friends laugh at your silliest jokes, put up with your worst moods, go along with your craziest ideas, and always see the best in you.

MY FEELINGS

Feelings are an emotion which result from circumstances around you and the thoughts you allow into your mind. They can also be a physical sensation. Much research has shown that our minds can help control the way we feel. Proverbs 14:13 says "When happiness is gone, sorrow is always there". So lets make up our minds to be happy.

Tick any goals relevant to you and add your own.

I always wake up happy.

I feel a sense of love towards everyone and I show it through kindness.

I am positive towards everyone and everything because being negative never helped anyone feel better.

I am in control of my thoughts and my feelings.

I am always given a choice and I choose to be happy.

_____

_____

_____

_____

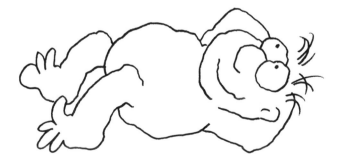

When you are at peace with yourself, any place is home.

MY FEELINGS

Describe how you have decided to take control of your feelings from now on.

_____

_____

_____

Happiness is like a butterfly.
The more you chase it, the more it eludes you.
But if you turn your attention to other things, it comes
and sits softly on your shoulder.

CAREERS I'D LIKE TO TRY

A Career is more than just a job. Trying a career means trying to do something that interests you, and learning as much about it as possible. There's nothing wrong with changing your career if you lose interest in that field. Happy people are those who are doing jobs that they love or consider very worthwhile. Keep trying new careers until you find one that you enjoy.

Tick any that appeal to you.

Selling

Teaching

Building

Creating

Managing

Designing

Fixing

Cleaning

Exporting

Modelling

Speaking

Researching

Typing

Exploring

Experimenting

Surveying

Parenting

Nursing

Curing

Problem Solving

The race is not always to the swift, but to those who keep on running.

MY CAREER

Ways of trying different careers.

— *part time jobs*

— *holiday jobs*

— *volunteer work for charities and associations*

— *work in companies without pay*

— *assist someone with their work at home*

Describe the careers you would like to try.

_____

_____

_____

_____

_____

_____

_____

_____

No dreamer is ever too small,
no dream is ever too big.

LEISURE ACTIVITIES I'D LIKE TO DO

Your leisure time is an opportunity to try new activities, relax, meet new people and go new places. People who like to try new challenges are often more interesting and open minded. Would you like to be one of these people?

Tick any activities you'd like to try and add some of your own.

snow skiing	hot air ballooning	rafting
horseriding	pottery	kyaking
windsurfing	cooking	handball
triathalons	gardening	squash
karate	sightseeing	racquetball
tennis	photography	volleyball
indoor cricket	scuba diving	trampolining
roller skating	snorkeling	surfing
skate boarding	acting	trail riding
baseball	painting	
football	bike riding	
basketball		
netball		
jet skiing		
water skiing		
dancing		
mountain climbing		
hiking		
absailing		
sailing		
parachutting		
para sailing		
canoeing		

To be different is often a wonderful thing.

LEISURE ACTIVITIES

Write your own leisure goals here.

_____

_____

_____

_____

_____

Success is getting
up one more
time than you
fall.

THINGS I WANT TO LEARN ABOUT

Life is a learning process. When you stop learning you start dying mentally. You become bored and boring!

Concentrate on learning three things everyday in the following ways. First, try to read something new. Second, listen to the knowledge of other people and third, simply observe people.

But why not try to learn about one specific topic that interests you and become an expert on it. I've been told that if you read 1 hour each day on that topic within 5 years, you'll be an expert.

HOBBIES	CAREERS	SELF–IMPROVEMENT

_____

_____

_____

_____

_____

FAMOUS PEOPLE	SPORTS OR ACTIVITIES	COUNTRIES

_____

_____

_____

Give no thought to what lies behind, push on to what lies ahead.

THINGS I WANT TO LEARN ABOUT

NOTE   When you stop learning, you will soon neglect what you already know.

Prov. 19:27 (G.N.B.)

List any extra things you want to learn about here.

_____

_____

Knowledge is what you know.
Wisdom is what you do with what you know.

PEOPLE I'D LIKE TO MEET

The people with whom we work and play always have an influence on us. Make sure that you're associating with people who affect you positively. By this I mean those people who inspire you to improve yourself and your circumstances.

We all need some friends older and wiser than us, who aren't scared to tell us if we're on the wrong path. We also need some friends to whom we can look up to.

NOTE   Keep company with the wise and you will become wise. If you make friends with stupid people you will be ruined. *Prov. 13:20 (G.N.B.)*

List the names of the people you'd like to meet.

It's not always what you know, but sometimes who you know.

PEOPLE I'D LIKE TO LEARN FROM

Truly successful people are always happy to help and advise you. Many people are too proud to admit that someone else could answer all their questions.

Don't let pride stop you from talking to and writing to successful people and asking for their advice. You might be amazed at what you learn.

NOTE   Get all the advice you can, and you will succeed; without it you will fail.

Prov. 15:22 (G.N.B.)

Example: Explorers, Scientists, Authors, Ministers, Celebrities, Business Magnates, Millionaires, Politicians, Sports Stars, Entertainers.

List the names of people you'd like to learn from.

You are the same today
as you will be five years from now,
except for two things —
The People You Meet and
The Books You Read

WAYS I'D LIKE TO SERVE MY COMMUNITY

If we all gave a little of our time to help in our community, what a great place it would be. Don't wait for everyone else to start, just get involved straight away. Most people follow by example, and it could be your example that leads them to help too.

IDEAS

Organizations to join

Clubs to support and assist

Festivals to participate in

Working bees to attend

Elderly people to visit

Charities to fundraise for

Rubbish to remove

Describe the ways in which you'd like to serve your community.

_____

_____

_____

Many hands make light work.

WAYS I'D LIKE TO SERVE MY COUNTRY

Describe the ways in which you'd like to serve your country.

IDEAS

Learn about politics

Express my views to my local member of Parliament

Defend my country in times of war so join the army reserve.

Help keep it clean

Do my job with 100% effort

Assist people in need

Build patriotism

Encourage others to do their best

_____

_____

_____

_____

_____

_____

_____

Don't ask what your country can do for you.
Ask what you can do for your country.

BOOKS I'D LIKE TO READ

NOTE Homes are built on the foundation of wisdom and understanding. Where there is knowledge, the rooms are furnished with valuable, beautiful things.

Prov. 24:3 & 4 (G.N.B.)

PERSONAL GROWTH

Think And Grow Rich — Napoleon Hill (254 pages).
The Psychology Of Winning — Denis Waitley (234 pages).
Move Ahead With Possibility Thinking — Robert Schuller (220 pages).
The Greatest Secret In The World — Og Mandino (163 pages).
See You At The Top — Zig Ziglar.

FINANCE AND WEALTH

The Richest Man In Babylon — George Clason
Acres of Diamonds — Russell H. Conwell (63 pages).

SPIRITUAL

The Bible
More Than A Carpenter — Josh McDowell (128 pages).
The Screwtape Letters — C.S. Lewis
Learning And Living — John Blanchard (192 pages)
Looking For The Answer — John Benton (91 pages)
Peace With God — Billy Graham

Tick the books you'd like to read and add others when recommended.

_____

_____

_____

_____

If you think education is expensive,
you ought to try ignorance.

BOOKS I'D LIKE TO READ

RELATIONSHIPS

Love — *Leo Buscaglia*
The Positive Family — *Arvella Schuller (137 pages)*
The Double Win — *Denis Waitley (215 pages)*

MENTAL

Superlearning — *Ostrander & Schroeder*
(313 pages)
As A Man Thinketh — *James Allen*

EMOTIONAL

Gift From The Sea — *Anne Morrow Lindbergh*
(140 pages)
Can You Trust Your Emotions — *James Dobson*
(143 pages)

Tick the books you'd like to read and add others when recommended.

_____

_____

_____

_____

_____

_____

NOTE: Setting aside just 15 minutes a day will enable you to read up to 24 books in a year. Keep it up and you will have read 1,000 books in your lifetime. That's the equivalent of going through college five times.

Don't hope for success,
Earn it!

PLACES I'D LIKE TO GO

List all the towns, cities, countries and native reserves you'd like to visit.

IDEAS

Within my city

Within my state

Other cities

Other states

Other countries or islands

_____

_____

_____

_____

_____

_____

_____

_____

_____

_____

Though we travel the world over to find the beautiful, we must carry it within us or we find it not.

PLACES I'D LIKE TO GO

List all the places you'd like to go for a holiday, to work, or to live for a while. Describe ways you could achieve this.

_____

_____

_____

_____

_____

_____

Travelling opens your eyes, your heart and your mind to the people of the world.

THINGS I'D LIKE TO OWN

Always keep in mind that owning 'things' will not make you happy. It's often more fun working towards achieving something, than actually having it. You will also get much more pleasure out of the things that you share, rather than the things that you keep to yourself.

NOTE   "Watch out and guard yourselves from every form of greed; because a person's true life is not made up of the things he owns, no matter how rich he might be."   *Luke 12:15 (G.N.B.)*

IDEAS

Musical instruments

Sporting equipment

Special clothing

Jewellery

Furniture

Cars

Homes or apartments

Electrical equipment

Books

Music

_____

_____

_____

_____

_____

_____

_____

Happiness is found in doing, not merely in possessing.

THE TRAITS I'D LIKE IN A PARTNER

The partner that you choose in life is one of the most important decisions you'll ever make. Take a lot of time to get to know people. Build friendships before you build intimate relationships. Every boyfriend or girlfriend you have, will affect you and influence you. Make sure that you want their type of influence. Get to know their character and see what common interests you share.

NOTE   If you have to choose between a good reputation and great wealth, choose a good reputation.

Prov. 22:1 (G.N.B.)

List any quality that you believe is important in a partner. Think about the common interests you should share.

Love is not measured by how many times we touch each other, but by how many times we reach each other.

PLANS I'D LIKE TO CARRY OUT

NOTE   We may make our plans, but God has the last word. *Prov. 16:1 (G.N.B.)*

Describe any plans you'd like to make a part of your life.

IDEAS

a daily fitness plan

a money saving plan

a plan to meet new people

a plan to listen to self-improvement cassettes

a beauty plan to look my best

a plan to always look my best

a plan to read a book each week

_____

_____

_____

_____

_____

Failing to plan
equals
planning to fail

SPECIAL PROBLEMS I'D LIKE TO SOLVE

List any special problems you'd like to start solving.

_____

_____

_____

_____

IDEAS I'D LIKE TO DEVELOP

Describe any ideas you'd like to start developing.

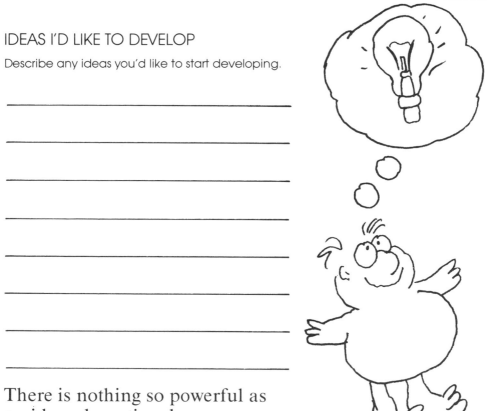

_____

_____

_____

_____

_____

_____

There is nothing so powerful as
an idea whose time has come.

TOP PRIORITY GOALS

It's important to have many goals in every area of your life. This helps you to clearly define the improvements that you're going to make. However, you must put all your goals in an order of importance. Otherwise, you won't know where to put your effort and concentration first. We can't do all things at once so we must pick just a few.

Select 10 goals from the previous pages which are most important to you, and write them below. We will continue to work with these goals in the coming pages. State by what date they will be achieved.

TODAYS
DATE

GOAL TO BE
ACHIEVED BY

1.

2.

3.

4.

5.

6.

7.

8.

9.

10.

Whatever the mind can CONCEIVE
and BELIEVE, it can ACHIEVE.

MORE TOP PRIORITY GOALS

Use this page only if you can't decide on 10 goals only. Otherwise, save this page to list your top 10 goals in 3 to 6 months time. This will help to show you just how often you need to be re-evaluating your top 10 priorities. If you find that your goals have changed after only one or two months, then re-evaluate more often.

Remember, the only thing that is constant in life is change!

TODAYS
DATE

GOAL TO BE
ACHIEVED BY

_____ 11. _____

_____ 12. _____

_____ 13. _____

_____ 14. _____

_____ 15. _____

_____ 16. _____

_____ 17. _____

_____ 18. _____

_____ 19. _____

_____ 20. _____

Man may not always make his goals, but his goals will always make the man.

If there were no valleys we would find no mountains to climb.

ADDING UP THE BENEFITS

NOTE: Before going any further, turn back to the "14 Guidelines For Goal Setting" and read them 3 times. Then take some extra paper and list 20 benefits for each goal that you're aiming to achieve.

Try listing 20 benefits of achieving your first goal on the list, here.

_____

_____

_____

_____

_____

_____

_____

_____

_____

_____

_____

_____

_____

_____

When the going gets tough,
the tough get going.

OBSTACLES I MUST OVERCOME

NOTE Sensible people will see trouble coming and avoid it, but an unthinking person will walk right into it and regret it later. *Prov. 22:3 (G.N.B.)*

There are two types of obstacles we must deal with —

1. There are PERSONAL OBSTACLES such as all the items listed on pages 12, 13 and 14, plus any bad habits or personality quirks we might have.

2. There are also OBSTACLES OUTSIDE OF OUR CONTROL such as other people and things.

Make two columns and try to list any obstacles that stand between you and the success you want to achieve. Once you've clearly defined what these obstacles are, it will be much easier to find ways to deal with them.

Getting out of bed early	fear of people
being out of town	people saying no
routine interupted	long late nights
boardom	not knowing what to say
desire to eat fattening foods	
having to cook for food	
eating on the road	

The strongest
trees are found
in the most
exposed places.

GOAL DETAILING

Take each goal and break it down into small "chunks" that you can start doing straight away. Number them in the order they should be attempted.

SAMPLE GOAL: — to get on better with my parents.

Chunks   — to ask my parents to calmly express what they expect from me.

— to talk openly with my parents about how I think they're treating me.

— to be patient each day and not expect changes overnight.

— to stay calm when we discuss something important.

— to ask my parents to listen to my opinions before they tell me what to do.

— to share my problems with my parents as they arise.

No-one is ever
whipped until
they quit -
in their own mind.

GOAL DETAILING

Break down your top priority goals into bite size chunks following the example on the opposite page.

_____

_____

_____

_____

_____

_____

_____

_____

_____

_____

_____

_____

(continued overleaf)

Life is either a daring adventure or nothing.

Helen Keller

_____

_____

_____

_____

_____

_____

_____

_____

_____

_____

_____

_____

_____

_____

Life is like a sandwich;
the more you add to it,
the better it becomes.

CONVERTING GOAL DETAILS TO AFFIRMATIONS

What is an affirmation? It is a very specific goal written in the positive, present tense.

Without action, nothing happens.

Knowledge without action will get you nowhere so you must commit yourself to take the first step of each goal, today. Write these steps in the positive present tense. For example, "<u>I am</u> asking my parents to calmly express what they expect from me each day this week." Notice that a time frame has been placed on the achievement of the goal, as well as using the <u>positive present tense.</u> This makes your sub–conscious believe that your goal is already being achieved.

Hence, your mouth starts to do the asking as it is directed by your sub–conscious. Carrying out your affirmations becomes second nature to your body. You convert all your goals to affirmations if you want to evoke action and get results.

A quitter never wins and a winner never quits.

CONVERTING GOAL DETAILS TO AFFIRMATIONS

Start writing your affirmations in the space below and use extra paper when necessary.

These affirmations need to be read at least three times per day and pictured in your mind. I suggest that you also write them on loose sheets of paper so that you can stick them up in your bedroom. You might also want copies for the back of the toilet door, the bathroom mirror, inside your diary, on the dashboard of your car and anywhere else you think you could read them often. Repetition and visualization is the key to making these affirmations really happen.

_____

_____

_____

_____

_____

_____

_____

(continued overleaf)

We become what we think about.

CONVERTING GOAL DETAILS TO AFFIRMATIONS

Write your affirmations in the space below and use extra paper when necessary.

_____

_____

_____

_____

_____

_____

We cannot discover new oceans unless we have the courage to lose sight of the shore.

WHAT TO DO NEXT

Let me summarize.

I have just said "Write out your goals, then break them down into chunks. Convert these chunks or details to affirmations and stick them up where you can see them often. Read them at least three times each day and "visualise yourself doing them."

"How is this going to make a difference?" you might ask.

Let me explain.

The first thing you must do is start playing mind games with yourself. That's right, it's a game! Let's say, for example, that you are having terrible arguments with your father. Just by writing down an appropriate affirmation such as "I'm getting on well with my father," won't change him, but it will focus your mind on the fact that it's possible.

Now you need to pretend, in your mind, that you are really getting on well with him and that you both feel good about it. Try to picture or visualise all the great conversations you are having, all the activities you are doing together and how happy you both are. Focus on how you both feel about this new comradeship and how it can continue to grow. Start to <u>expect</u> that it can exist and <u>believe</u> that it will.

There is no gain without pain.
But you'll certainly enjoy
the benefits.

72

WHAT TO DO NEXT

After playing these mind games with yourself, the next time you speak to him, your voice and tone will be a little different. It will take him by surprise. You need to continue to imagine these good situations and feelings at least three times a day. Spend a mere sixty seconds each time and feel confident about getting the required result.

Your father will see a definite change in you and start to wonder what is happening. His attitude to you will change and also his behaviour. You will have achieved your goal.

Remember, for things to change, you must change, or at least the thoughts in your mind must change.

Now what if this doesn't work the first time. Simple. If at first you don't succeed, try, try again! In fact you'll probably need to try at least seven times, and sometimes up to twenty one times, before you have formed your new attitude or habit. You'll need to give your father as many chances too. So don't get despondent and give up early. This is where your attitude becomes so important. You must keep your morale high and believe that this method works. Because it does!

Enthusiasm
Don't defuse it — use it.
Don't block it — unlock it.
You need it so feed it.

BE PERSISTENT!

If you get to the stage where you've tried a couple of times and are thinking about giving up, don't! Remind yourself that you must at least give yourself seven chances and remember that one of the main reasons for failing is lack of perseverance. You must persist if you want to succeed.

When you're feeling low, give some thought to a sporting star you admire, such as Pat Cash, Australia's number one male tennis player. Just think about the number of times he has had to practise his serve to get it just the way he wants it. I'm a tennis fan, so I often think about my 18 year old friend, Lisa O'Neil, going through her gruelling tennis training just to maintain her national ranking. Like most sporting stars, she has learned to visualise herself doing each stroke perfectly and does so often. No moments are wasted because as the body rests the mind works.

Every athlete has to develop a great belief in themselves just to be able to keep on keeping on. They must control their thoughts all the time. They need to remain positive when they lose, stay enthusiastic when they're injured and desire to win so badly that it drives them on to work harder and longer, and to learn to better use the incredible powers of their mind. That's persistence!

Sporting stars are prepared to give up most of their social time, the opportunity to do other sports and nearly all junk food to achieve fitness, skill and sporting success. What are you prepared to forego to achieve your goals? Write these things down.

Small opportunities are the beginning of great enterprises.

Triumph is made up of two words. TRY and UMPH.

PROBLEM SOLVING

Solving problems is a part of life, just like working and eating. People who are good at problem solving usually have a happier home and a more successful career than those who are slow to resolve their problems. The only people who don't have problems are dead.

The most important part of problem solving takes place in the mind. It's a matter of controlling your feelings and your thoughts to enable you to think clearly and logically. Then you can write out all the alternative solutions you have to choose from.

Solve your problems
or your problems will
dissolve you.

PROBLEM SOLVING

Ashleigh is my 18 month old niece. Sometimes her goal is to take the cat food out of the bowl because it looks so interesting. She takes a step towards it, but her mother reprimands her. She's facing her first problem, the prospect of punishment. What should she do, give up or go forward? She reviews her purpose, i.e. she wants to try all the new things around her. She has a good, strong reason for attempting to get the cat food which is on the floor. She decides she is prepared to take the reprimand to achieve her goal of the cat food. With dogged determination she moves towards it. That's problem solving!

So the steps you must consider are —

1. *How important is your goal? Is it more important than your problem?*

2. *How strong is your purpose for achieving that goal? Is it worth fighting for?*

3. *What are you prepared to do, or give up, to solve your problem?*

4. *Start writing down all the possible ways to solve your problem. Remove any that aren't in agreeance with your personal standards.*

5. *Select one option. Write down the most likely consequences. Do they violate anyone else's rights. If yes, choose another option. If not, go ahead and try it. Don't be afraid to fail, even if it means trying many options one after the other.*

6. *Resign yourself to succeed.*

7. *Move ahead and be prepared to solve more problems.*

Obstacles are what you see when you take your eyes off the goal.

HOW TO RELEASE TENSION

If problem solving creates stress or tension within you, relieve this by doing one or more of the following activities.

1. Go and do some vigorous activity to assist all body muscles to relax.

   Some suggestions are — swim as fast and far as you can in a safe swimming area.

   — walk briskly or jog as far as you can.

   — do an aerobics class.

   — dance vigorously in your home until tired.

   — skip with a skipping rope for as long as possible.

   — ride a bike or row a boat until you're tired.

2. Go to the beach or a park and sit quietly. Try to remove all thoughts from your mind and be at peace with yourself and God.

3. Write a letter to any other person involved in your problem and express exactly how you feel.
   Don't send this letter! Don't even consider it! It is a means to vent your feelings. If you want to send a letter, give yourself several days to think clearly before writing it.

4. Go to your local library and find a book on self improvement or problem solving. Sit quietly and read. Try to learn about yourself, your reactions and your ability to handle problems.

5. Go and visit someone who needs your help or a willing ear. Listen to their problems and think of ways you can best assist them. Don't talk about your problem. Try to focus on your friend's needs.

6. Clean up a cupboard that really needs some attention from you. Put your energy and concentration into the task.

7. Rearrange your room or your wardrobe.

8. Cook a meal for your family or friends.

9. Write a diary about how you are feeling and how you would like to feel. Make a list of all the things that you like in life, especially things that make you feel great.

What you do with your problem is far more important than what your problem does to you.

HOW TO RELEASE TENSION

10. *Write a poem or short story to express how you feel.*

11. *Read a good book which takes your mind off your problem.*

12. *Start a creative project, such as making something, designing something or describing a good idea you'd like to follow up.*

To be upset over what you don't have is to waste what you do have.

WAYS I WILL RELIEVE TENSION

Describe the steps you will take to assist you to cope with any stress or tension you feel.

_____

_____

_____

_____

_____

There's no such thing as try. You either do or you don't.